THE CITY

John Barnie

GOMER

First impression—1993

ISBN 0 86383 996 7

This volume is published with the support of the Welsh Arts Council

*Printed by J. D. Lewis and Sons Ltd.,
Gomer Press, Llandysul, Dyfed*

Acknowledgements

Section LIX is a translation from an unpublished diary by Gustav Jensen, known as "Gustavs dagbog". It describes the loss with all hands of the barque *Timaru* off the coast of north-west Jutland in 1907. Reproduced here by kind permission of the diary's present owner, Gustav Brun.

My thanks to Pamela Stewart and Helle Michelsen for their criticism.

'Mother' and 'Inhuman' first appeared in *Poetry Canada Review*.

CONTENTS

Every generation must build its own city

Antonio Sant'Elia

I

When I can't sleep I lie in the dark, eyes open and unblinking, staring upwards. As the hours pass, I feel a fine patina of dust collecting on their glistening surfaces. But I have no wish to see with them: I've let the city enter my mind.

II

—Bloomin English. Your girls have no grace, they walk with the gait of cows. Yesterday him next door called me a bloody foreigner. I've lived here twenty years. At the end of the war I led my men across the mountains into Italy. It was clear it was all over. We'd listened to your Churchill: "Brave patriots of Jugoslavia, England is behind you. Fight on." But they parachuted the weapons to the partisans, not to us, and our men had to scavenge for arms, killing Germans, killing partisans. A Mauser was as gold in the hand. At the end my men had nothing to eat, they eat grass. Have you ever lived on grass for weeks. The weak and the wounded were left behind. We could carry no one over the mountains. Some begged to be shot. Because of the Germans. "Radomir it has to be done." My friend. He lay raised on one arm. He bent his head toward the ground like a girl. I reach out with my revolver until it is a hair breadth from his neck. Then fired. He give a jolt like electric shock, then he's still. What is the difference between life and death.

When I was a boy before the war I was a hunter. Each animal I killed so beautiful. A hawk hurtling across the sun as I fired. Then it tumbled over and fell and hit and bounced over the ground. My friend, I retrieved it and gathered it in my hand and smoothed out its feather. I looked for a long time past the golden circle of its iris into the eye. It was so dark I felt cold.

When I killed him I stood over my friend with the gun in my hand. Radomir it has to be done.

When we got to Italy we gave ourselves to the British troops. Our friends. But we were betrayed. I began with two hundred men over the mountains. In Italy twenty-nine. They betrayed us. "Major, Major, you know what they will do to us." My men were prodded into cattle wagons by guns. They were crying. "Major, Major." I heard later some ripped open the boards, they threw themselves from the train onto the track. Better death. "Radomir it has to be done." I was spared because I spoke Russian, I could interpret in Berlin. And he call me a bloody foreigner. Bloomin English.

The city has engaged him as one of its kind. Now he works as a wages clerk behind frosted panes in an inner office of a big chocolate factory.

4

"Come on Rady, haven't you got those chits ready yet?" "I'm coming. I'm coming." Bloomin English.

At night he stretches out in the chair, concentrating his lugubrious, crumbling face on a Science Club book about how the universe may expand for ever, receding with its lights. Radomir! Glad to be alone among the silent distances between stars.

III

By day, cars are colour, sheen, depth, exhaust, impatience, kinetic, slowing in lines at traffic lights, hands tapping on the steering wheel, come on, come bloody on.

Pedestrians peer up and down the streets, dodge in and out. What you using for brains. Stupid bastard.

On hot midsummer days, air shimmers off car roofs in streams, light flashes blind off windscreens. Jesus.

Cars are our will to be.

But at night as I lie in the dark of my room, cars are effaced to sound. Beyond midnight a continuous roar, a race through traffic lights, the changing up and down of gears, engines revving, moulded by, echoing from the city streets.

Two o' clock, three o' clock. I can't say when, but it's over, the noise, the background glare of the city exhausted, stretched out until, tenuous, it snaps. The silence like nothing on Earth, highlighted by the moan of a single car.

IV

He approaches across the bridge. Below, the dirty river spreads thinly over cobbles and a half-submerged supermarket trolley. As he gets close, he already holds out his hand, palm down, the thin wrist looking as if it had been jammed clumsily and impatiently up into the sleeve of his greasy jacket. Come on Jack, that'll bloody do, you're nothing special.

It could be that we will merely glance at each other as we pass. But I know this isn't so. At ten paces he holds out his hand.

—Look at this Guv. Issa rose. See this. Issa rose of my life.

In the middle of the veined back of his hand is a sore, exfoliating in crust at the edges, soft and petal pink within, centred with the yellow pus of his rose's pistil.

—Issa rose of my life. That is.

—Yes.

He doesn't want anything. Not on the bum. Issa rose. Cultivated this for years. For *years*. Till it flowered. Ah whadafuck. He stumbles on over the bridge, already lost in the drowning noise of the mid morning traffic.

—Issa rose. Rose of my life. Issa rose. That is.

V

—Fucking blacks. Don't tell me about fucking blacks. When I was in the Navy—Her Majesty's fucking *Royal* Navy, not your Merchant crap—I been to Africa and seen them. They were living in fucking *trees*. And now they come over here and the fucking do-good politicians tell us how *we* have to treat *them* and let *them* take *our* fucking jobs. Send the bastards back where they come from. Send them back to the jungle where they fucking belong. They got no rights here. Have you seen how they live. Keep chickens in the fucking kitchen. Chicken shit everywhere. Using the doors for firewood. They're fucking ignorant, that's what they are. The government must have been off their fucking rockers when they let them in. I can't stand them. And I'll tell you something. I don't know anyone who can. They give me the creeps. Fucking hell. Look at that. That's what I call tits. How'd you like to get up that. Come on over here darling. Drop your knickers, Brian's here. Fucking hell. Give us a roll, I'm all out. That all you got. Old Holborn's dried cow shit. Didn't you know. Come on, drink up. Two pints Billy and don't piss in it. I been out there and I seen them. Don't talk to me about fucking blacks. They were living in trees.

VI

A man clambers down an iron ladder into the sewer. The shaft of light he's let in is blinding to the rats that scuttle in all directions as his boots clank on the rungs. But only for a moment. As he pauses in his waders in the stream of effluent, rats emerge from the crevices with needle-bone teeth. The man whistles a tune that was popular forty years ago. It's his way of getting a hold. He deliberately splashes down the bed of the stream, feet planted out. It gives him balance, a surer grip on the bricks beneath the soft, sliding layer of sludge under his feet.

With a large hand-torch he inspects the walls as he goes. The beam of light sweeps across the rats that flash back with the tiny points of their eyes.

The man pauses again at the junction of the main sewer and a tributary. The effluent swells here, ripples a supple brown in the light of his torch. A slight steam rises from it, almost as if it were the visible stench, clouding the farther recesses of the endless tunnel.

This man knows more about the city than most. How it lives and breathes on its own. He knows he is its servant, fuelling it, fulfilling its needs. We are not, as we think, its purpose.

He shines his torch up and down the walls of the tributary tunnel. It curves rapidly away to the right into black. The true rivers of the city, flowing and rippling under the dripping bricks with their companionable rats. Above his head, though he cannot hear them, people walk the pavements, cars weave in the narrow streets. The sun is shining and everyone says what a wonderful day. Sparrows and pigeons dart in-and-out among passing feet for scraps of bread, crisps, hot dogs, chip wrappers. The pigeons croo-croo on their shock-red legs, jerk their heads, peck here, peck there, as if they can't help it and anything underfoot might be something to eat.

An old lady on a bench by the pigeon- and starling- and car-grimed cathedral under the trees has a crumpled bag of crumbs. On the ground beside her, a black travelling bag made of mock leather, its broken handles tied up with string.

—Come on darlings. Come on. Come to mother.

She scatters crumbs nearer and nearer her hand.

—Come on. Come to mother.

The birds approach, nodding their heads, jerking the iridescent green-and-mauve spilled-petrol flashes at their necks.

—Come on to mother.

9

One stretches out to peck and almost touches the hand. But before it dibs its beak she has grabbed it below the head, hauled it into her lap, placed her left hand at the base of its neck just below the shoulders, and screwed once, twisting hard.

In the noise of the traffic I can't hear it click.

She stuffs the bird still quivering its shocked, useless nerves and fluttering wings into the travel bag. She doesn't look up or around and walks sharply off.

—Did you see that old bag. Some people are desperate.

As the old woman walks away, the man in the sewer shines his torch once more, carefully, across the vaulting at the junction. She passes directly over his head, over the effluent and the rats, the twisting, glistening, streaming dark viscera of the city.

VII

I was writing one morning at the kitchen table, hardly aware of the traffic-grind outside, as if its constancy was an obverse of silence. I hardly heard the bump or sharp application of brakes. But I heard the high shriek.

Curious, I got up and went to the window and looked down from the first floor into the street. A car was stopped below me and by its offside wheel a boy lay on his back, very still and untouched on the tarmac. He was thirteen or fourteen.

At his side was his Turkish mother in long drab clothes, with a white head-scarf. She threw up her hands, slapped them on her knees, slapped her cheeks and screamed in a vortex. Then slapped her knees, rocked to-and-fro, let the scream rise again, spiralling. Without any thought. Without control.

The driver stood at the front of the car. He was shaken and silent, not knowing what to do. When he left home it had been an ordinary day.

VIII

As we enter the plane, Vivaldi is being played over the intercom. There is an almost silent, slow moving but intense need to get to our seats. The stewardesses are smiling, welcoming us on board. Baggage is stowed in the plastic compartments above our heads and clicked shut.

I settle in, adjust and lock the seat belt. The violins and violas flutter like marvellous mechanical birds to soothe us. Like the dunka-dunk dunk, dunka-dunk dunk of the disco music on the pig farm, in the vast airy building where the fetor of ammonia is a salvolatile, where the head of each pig in a metal stall is held on a short chain at the neck so it never can be jerked more than two feet from the trough.

The air is filled with their screeches and squeals, their grunts, their poking and rooting in the gutter of the troughs, the fury of their jerks on the chains. Dunka-dunk dunk, dunka-dunk dunk.

Vivaldi is switched off. It was a pretence, after all. *Ping. Ping.* We're warned about seat belts, no smoking. The pilot revvs the engines from a whine to a roar. The plane shudders as it's turned through a hundred and eighty degrees to be powered down the approach to the runway. Over the intercom, an air hostess explains where the escape hatches are, how to inflate the life-jackets, how oxygen masks will float down above our heads if the cabin pressure fails.

Stewardesses mime to her words along the cabin, pointing forward, to the sides and aft at the doors. Our ceremonial dancers.

The plane pauses. It has reached the runway. The engines are raised to a crescendo, the fuselage shudders with the restraint of the power. It can't be long. Then release. Everything rushes past us. Indifferent. Farewell. Until, climbing steadily, we lift and the juddering stops.

We bank, so the city slides into my window and the sky glides down into the one across the gangway. We swing round into our course, still climbing. There's no more Vivaldi. Music of the museum. Only the roar of the engines, our own merciless music out of which we must make our peace.

IX

—Jeg er hendes ben. Jeg er hendes *ben*. I'm her legs.

Hr Hansen looks at me with his glum, anxious face. His wife, with her arthritic hips and knees, has just been on a visit.

—Don't worry, Willy. I'm coping. The neighbours are very kind. I can get everything I need. I'm alright.

—Jeg er hendes ben, Hr Hansen explains again, holding on to the metal pole on wheels that looks like a hatstand and supports a plastic bag which slowly fills with his yellow urine.

He had come into hospital for a routine operation. Haemorrhoids. But the doctors had found something else. Somethig wrong with his bladder. And now he must walk (—You must exercise, Hr Hansen!) up and down the room in his dressing gown, with this hatstand on wheels and the bag of urine exposing his shame. Looking glum.

—I do all her shopping, clean the house. We've been married for thirty-nine years. She can hardly walk. I do everything for her. How will she get on without me. Jeg er hendes *ben*.

Hr Hansen grumbles about the food. Do you see this. Do you call this food. It's hardly cooked. It's not even warm. The nurses are kind. Oh come on Hr Hansen, try it. It's lovely. You'll like it. Pah.

He pushes his plate away, presiding over his enormous belly.

One evening the doctor comes in. She is young.

—I'm going to have to change your catheter, Hr Hansen. Alright? Lie back now and let the nurse undo your pyjamas.

I look away. Hr Hansen and I share a room on the eighth floor, with a big window overlooking the vast display of grey city buildings. As the doctor prepares, I look out to inspect the world from which Hr Hansen and I have been temporarily withdrawn.

—Oh. Oh. Oh.

I have to look.

Hr Hansen is trying to urge himself up over the massive pro-tuberance of his belly, he is trying to protest. But a nurse gently presses him down.

—Oh. Oh. Ohhh.

—I'm sorry Hr Hansen. I know this hurts. But it has to be done. If we don't change the catheter it will become infected.

—Aaah.

She pushes the catheter slowly deeper into his penis.

—Aaah. Oh. Ohhh. Ohh *God.*

At last it is over. Hr Hansen lies back and lets the nurse pull up his pyjamas.

—Oh it didn't hurt that bad last time.

—I'm sorry Hr Hansen. It's the first time I've done it.

—Don't they teach you anything in medical school. Where's the usual Doctor. I've never had pain like that. I'm going to complain.

—It's alright Hr Hansen. It's over now.

—Where is he. I'm going to complain.

The doctor and the nurses leave us to ourselves. It is quiet in the gathering dusk.

In the grey evening light of the city I can see the profile of his face as it lies back exhausted among the pillows. He stares hard at the ceiling. Sweat prickles his brow.

Then he turns slowly and cumbrously, shifting his bulk and the plastic tube, so he lies on his side away from me. And cries.

At first I don't realise it. There are no sobs, no sounds. Just an intense shiver in his breath as if he is suddenly very, very cold. I turn and look towards him across the gulf. His whole body shivers as he struggles with the great cry that is within him. *I am alone.*

X

—Yes you can talk. Do you think I come here because I have nothing better to do. That I wanted to leave my country and my home. Do you think I'm here because I like it. There is no faith here, no truth. Only lies. When I look at you I see that you are a lie. When I look into your eyes I know what is there. Hollowness and ashes like the Dead Sea fruit. You see, I am not afraid to say it to your face. You are a lie. You are hollow as the fruit. Hollowness and ashes.

As I listen, I measure the distance between myself and this man and the large empty wine bottle on the table between us. His head glistens under the light.

—You think I wanted to come here, to be here, to live here, to look every day into the face of a lie like yours.

If he goes on, I know that one us will smash the other in the face. I estimate his speed against mine in reaching for the bottle whose green glass has no other purpose now except as a weapon.

—Bastard. Bastard. Bastard. Bastard.

XI

—I saw you.

The phone is put down with a click before I have time to answer. I lie back and absorb myself again in the sounds of the night.
People drinking on the balcony next door talk in low voices. Someone laughs. There is a chink of glasses.

The phone rings again and I pick the receiver up and listen. There is a moment of silence.

—I saw you.

—What do you mean?

—Never mind.

I'm sure I can hear his quiet, contained amusement. There's a background noise that might come from a pub. Then the phone is put down.

He walks back with the slight swagger that comes from an evening's good drinking, sits with his companions and takes a long draught from his glass of beer. He settles the glass on the beer mat, then places both hands squarely on the table, elbows raised, as if he has changed his mind and is about to lever himself up. Then he laughs. A broad, dry, open, mock-generous laugh, like someone acting in a play. It is not directed at his companions. It has no meaning.

—Come on. Drink up.

XII

The restaurant at the top of the Rotunda, the city's highest building, revolves slowly. As the guests eat, they can see the city spread out beneath and beyond them in a complete circle. Three hundred and sixty degrees of the city and its meaning.

Most don't think of it, taken up by the novelty, wondering how it's done, making jokes about the waiters hopping on and off to the wrong tables—''Sorry Sir, Madam.''

But the architect who designed this was a serious man. He wanted those who dined here to come and see, for once, what the city means.

At first, it is familiar. The diminutive streets, like the ones we walked down to get here. Also the spires of the city, seen clearly for the first time.

—That must be Saint Michael's.

—No, Saint Mark's, surely.

—Do you think so?

But the city goes on. Yes, that must be the Habersham Building and that the new development down at the Docks. The restaurant slowly rotates through a circle and now we're back again.

—Yes it must be Saint Mark's.

But we must do better. The architect was a serious man. As we eat and stare through the window we gradually become silent. The city extends to the curve of the horizon. It ends in grey heat and exhaust haze in all directions. It is so vast, one mind cannot comprehend it. It spreads everywhere, lazily. Yet it is turned in on itself as on a complex thought, meditating a problem which, if solved, would have no application.

XIII

—Ak ja! It'll all be over in a hundred years. No one will be alive to remember this pain and worry then. That's what I used to say to Harry. It'll all be over in a hundred years.

It used to make him so angry.

"I know it'll all be over in a hundred years, but in the meanwhile *I'm* bloody *here*."

I had to laugh. And that made it worse. "It's no joke. What people have to endure in this *one* bloody city."

"Oh Harry, don't take on so. It'll all be over in a hundred years."

"Go to bloody *Hell*."

And I'd fold my arms and look at him and smile.

"Yes you're right, you stupid bloody bitch."

He'd go out and get drunk then.

Drink was his medicine. His search for a cure.

"It'll all be over in a hundred years."

Ak ja!

XIV

There's a thunder storm about to break over the city. From my bed on the eighth floor of the central hospital I watch it build up, darkening, through the afternoon. A swirling, deepening cloud mass, breached at one point by the sun in an intense spot of liquid silver.

There's nothing else to do, and the sky demands attention.

The first rain comes in a curtain, swaying in an ogee shape across the distant churches. Then nearer. Then banging and slashing at the panes, blearing the view.

Lightning flashes at three separate points. Delicate, many-tongued, dancing. Thunder whip-cracks, electrifying the air.

The stinging rain beats people off the streets into doorways, into cafés with steamed up windows. It beats down hard and rebounds six inches off the pavements. The gutters choke. And cars grind to a crawl.

The lightning flickers like an eyelash's kiss. Faint and innocent, hardly daring to prowl.

The air grows less oppressive but the sky is still dangerous like steel lit from within. The lightning breaks round the unaccommodating buildings, teases itself out, shivers down conductors like a disappearing trick. The thunder retreats with a threat. Ta-rrum.

People emerge, look up and carry on. Back in offices and shops they notice the neon lights seem weak again. Hadn't it gone dark!

The storm rolls itself away like a fairground show packing up. No fuss. Professional.

The sun streams through the first break in the cloud and suddenly the spires of all the city's churches are gleaming wet gold. Their weather-vanes and flags strut and fly in the wind.

XV

The city at night is a galaxy, the concentrate of power. Flying over it, we can see why we come. Strings of lights, leads of lights, towers of lights are flung in all directions, tangled in dense knots of power.

The black space of a park is something stamped out. It doesn't exist. Only the lights give a sense of identity. We have built them. Look at the cars, streams of tail-lights, streams of headlights. Coming and going.

In the all-night bars, the mind begins to flag.

—Yeh. I fucked up.

In the shiny diners with giant windows that let us see how lonely we are, the insomniacs stare out, stare past the ghost image of themselves in the reflection, to the yellow-lit streets.

One man inhales from a cigarette. Then blows out the smoke, slowly. His head is propped on one cupped hand, the other, with the cigarette, fingers the handle of the white cup.

He looks at his ghost self in the window looking back at him.

—I doubt any man will come out alive. *Give up*. For Chrissakes.

The airliner banks and decelerates, lowering itself onto the city. The passengers become alert. These visible signs of power are welcoming.

When they land, there will be lights wherever they go. Needless and symbolic, therefore essential.

XVI

In the wholesale tobacco warehouse, Mr Allworthy, the foreman, shuffles on his painful feet in their specially-made shoes.

—Kenny, where's those Craven A?

—They're coming. They're coming, Mr Allworthy. I've only got one pair of hands.

—Well get a move on then. I asked you for them an hour ago.

—Alright. Alright.

Mr Allworthy shuffles back to his office, following his bulbous purple nose. He doesn't like to scold. He can hardly walk for arthritis and holds his head permanently on his chest, so when he wants to look up he has to bend back from the waist. In his office, which is like a wooden sentry-box with chits and reminders pinned to the walls, he takes a handkerchief from his brown storeman's coat. He buries his face in it and bugles with his nose.

—Tea-break!

It's an old joke.

Kenny has disappeared behind shelves stacked with cigarettes, trundling his porter's trolley; good at forgetting.

—Kenny. Ken-*ny*.

Now the checkers are impatient. He is holding them up.

—*Whadisit.*

—There's no Park Drive or Benson & Hedges.

—And where's those Craven A?

—Alright. Alright. I'm coming. I'm not a blinking slave.

—Well get a move on then.

—Alright. Alright. Blinking slave driver.

He ambles with his trolley up a ramp at the back of the building, banging it through two metal-covered doors.

The checkers stand about chatting, holding blue order forms on clip-boards.

—Ooh I got a glimpse of Angie's stocking tops.

—No you didn't. Cheeky beggar.

She shimmies her dress down, mock demure.

Bang. Bang.

Kenny comes back, demonstrably, through the swing doors. He sways down the ramp with an over-stocked trolley, peering round the side with the shock of his head.

When he reaches the checkers, he upends the cases in a broken column on the floor.

21

—Ken-*ny*.

—*I* couldn't help it.

—Yes you could.

—What's up. Anything wrong?

—It's alright Mr Allworthy.

—Ah.

—Come on Kenny. Get them on the stacks.

—Alright. Alright. I'm not a blinking slave.

—Well get a move on then.

The checkers elbow him aside, impatient to get on with their orders. They rip open the cases and reach in for packets of 200. One glances at her watch: half an hour to tea-break.

Kenny is gone.

XVII

Her husband has multiple sclerosis. He can only sit now in a wheelchair, he cannot speak and is nearly blind.

Death. It would be a blessing, the neighbours say, for them both.

But, no, she says, not so. She does not feel this, watching him slumped there, thick veins like rivers tumbling in gorges between the kopje'd knuckles of his hands. Not so.

Since she found Jesus, everything has changed.

—*God is good to me, God is so good to me*
I don't serve Him as I should
I don't deserve all of this good
So many things are not as they should be
But God is good to me.

—Amen!

—Amen!

—Amen! Dear brothers and sisters. God *is* good to every *one* of us who will listen. You know, if you'd let Jesus enter your heart, it'd make such a difference, it'd make such a change.

You know, I used to drink. I used to fornicate. I used to beat my wife and children. Until one night I got on my knees and cried—Jesus! Oh Jesus!

You know, I was at the end of the tether. I'd been down every road. And it was a dead end.

But that night, that night, I got on my knees and prayed. And I found Jesus. I entered a great shining sea of His peace. His peace. His peace. *His* peace!

—Amen!

—Amen!

—And now I'm going to tell you
How I got over (How I got) over, my Lord
And my soul looked back and wondered (wondered, wondered)
How I get over, my Lord.

Yes, I did get over. Over my troubles, over my sins, over my hopelessness. Dear brothers and sisters, Jesus saves. Yes He does. Jesus saves, Jesus *saves.*

—Jesus. Jesus. Jesus. Oh Jesus!

—O yes!

—Jesus. Jesus. Oh Jesus.

—Dear friends. Do I have a witness. I want to tell you. I'm so happy

23

here tonight. Do I have a witness. Will anybody here pray with me tonight.

And the woman feels her soul at her eyes. Yes. Yes.

Tears well over her cheeks onto her blouse, dripping and blotting the thin pages of the hymn book.

—Have mercy. Have mercy Jesus.

—*Happy day, happy day*
When Jesus washed my sins away
He taught me how to watch and pray
And live rejoicing every day
Happy day, happy day
When Jesus washed my sins away.

The woman stands holding the hymn book, but she cannot see the blurred, slithery words. Happy *day* Jesus.

She sees the great city where she lives as if from a height and its subdued river winding among the buildings and streets.

She sees beyond, where the river leaves the city and enters the sea, brilliant with constantly glittering light. And in the midst, Jesus. He raises His arms. *I am the way.*

XVIII

The pictures on the walls are a lifetime's haphazard collection, some by minor artists, none very good.

On the china cabinet with its latticed panels, photographs of children, grandchildren, cousins, nieces and nephews, the more recent ones coloured. The faces are friendly, well-disposed, though some in sepia offer smiles from the dead. The young have suffered this for an old lady they hardly know.

The books in the bookcase are Victorian and Edwardian editions that peter out with Siegfried Sassoon.

—Dickens, above all, of the English novelists. Then the poets. Wordsworth, of course, the best of Shelley, poor Keats. Byron—not quite a classic, I always think. Browning for the monologues, but not that dreadful *Ring*. Tennyson, the lyricist:

> *The splendour falls on castle walls*
> *And snowy summits old in story;*
> *The long light shakes across the lakes,*
> *And the wild cataract leaps in glory.*

Blow, bugle, blow, set the wild echoes flying,
Blow, bugle; answer, echoes, dying, dying, dying.

She takes a book from the shelves.

—Have I shown you?

Arthur Staples, *The Bitter Draft*.

A soft-covered edition.

Inside, the inscription: "From Arthur to Hilda, with affection. Haddsleigh, 1925."

—Poor Arthur. He died. He so wanted to be a poet. But he was no good, and knew. What is it like, dying and knowing you've failed?

She takes the book and puts it back on the shelf.

XIX

—Yer. Think you're clever. Bastard. Three times round the world, that's me. Three times round the world. And I wouldn't give you tuppence. Yer. Keep your travel. Keep your Costa del Sol. Yer. Keep your charter flights and cruises. Fat bastards going out all pink. Yer. Coming back brown from a bottle. Yer. Mister Clever. "Think I'll check the time on my twenty-four hour Rolex watch." Yer. What's the time in Hong Kong, then. San Francisco. Yer. Look down your nose at me. Think I'm shite. Yer. Shite comes from somebody's ass. Yer. What's that make you.

XX

Demolition workers blow up a factory by the railway tracks. Grimed redbrick with the firm's name in relief and the date, 1890. "Let her go." We see puffs of dust. *Boom.* The face of the building ripples with cracks, holds for a moment before the collapse. *Voom.* A sun-flash on glass shatters. Bricks clatter and tinkle. The dust spurts sideways, rushes up in a violent grey flower. Rats that have not been killed shiver in sewers. They will emerge from the rubble at night. Pause. Sniff. Crouch. And run across the sandy, clinkered, willow-herbed waste land, under the broken perimeter fence to the tracks. The shining fast line to the city. Here comes an express. It whispers and twangs invisibly through the steel. *Bam.* Lights, wheels, faces, lights, faces. EEEEEOOOoooo. The tail lamps dwindle rapidly like malevolent eyes.

XXI

It's six o' clock on a winter Saturday afternoon. The big store in the city. Last customers drift toward the doors, eyeing the goods in shining display cases. The girls behind the counters are exhausted and bored.

A doorman in a green frock-coat and green top hat flicks back his sleeve to look at his watch. He holds his arm parallel to his face, lets the white-gloved hand dangle.

Then snaps it back, coming to attention as a middle-aged couple stroll toward the exit.

The doorman swings open one of the steel-and-glass doors and ushers them out with a slight bow and a sweep of his left gloved hand.

—Goodnight, Sir. Madam.

—Thank you. Goodnight.

Stupid prats.

—Is that the lot?

—Think so.

The doorman reaches up, reaches down, snaps the bolts into position. He glances at the shop lights across the street, the silhouettes of hurrying shoppers, himself as a slim, unbelievable glaze in the door-glass.

He turns and does a ballroom glide across the thick plush of the carpet. Left hand tucked at the back of an invisible woman, right crooked up and out as he gazes into her eyes.

—I don't want another Saturday like that.

—Too bloody right.

The girls and the doorman stand around. Free to go, they pause and take their time.

Not entirely dissatisfied.

XXII

—Brrgh. It's bloody cold mate. Brrgh. It's cold. Eh mate.

I shoulder past into the pub. No bouncers yet. But the bar is getting crowded.

I inhale the smell of beer and tobacco smoke whirled round under the high ceiling by the blades of gleaming brass fans.

Dunk-a-dunk dunk, dunk-a-dunk dunk-dunk, dunk-a-dunk dunk.

I queue at the bar and reach over shoulders for a pint, take it back sipping from the rim while my eyes search for a seat.

There's a small table and a single slatted chair against a wall.

Across from me, in the window, are two men in their twenties with cropped almost shaved hair. And a woman whose skirt has slid to her thighs.

The men are in jeans and faded T-shirts, but the woman is wearing a grey two-piece costume and has a briefcase under her chair. She is reading a report as they talk and makes corrections or comments in the margin with a ball-point pen. I can't quite hear what they say. But it's jokey and desultory. I can see from their faces.

The men look into the street, scanning passers-by without interest.

A woman in her late thirties walks past, casting a glance through the window. Her eyes touch the eyes of one of the men and he beckons her in.

—Look at that. Come here darling.

But she was already turning into the side entrance of the pub. I lose sight of her for a moment, then the door opens and she reappears. She has tight jeans and stiletto heels. She turns and closes the door.

The man who called to her leans back over his chair, stretching his left hand back and open, palm up. His head is pressed against the wooden rim of the chair.

—I'm all yours tonight darling. Do with me what you like.

She leans over him, familiarly, smiling, right hand resting on the arm of the chair. With her left, she presses a crumpled crisp packet into his palm. He closes his fingers round it.

—No thanks love. I'm all tied up tonight.

The woman pushes herself up off the arm of the chair. She steps briskly toward the bar but turns to look at him, flashing a smile.

The man brings his hand slowly forward, raising himself in the chair to examine the blue packet. He half turns in his seat.

—Cor thanks a lot.

—You're welcome.

He shows his friend. Look at that.

—Tomorrow then.

Turning to look at her. Fluttering his eyelashes.

She laughs again and gives another brilliant smile. Slips into the crowd at the bar.

—Bloody cow.

But in lower tones. To no one. Sliding down in his chair, settling to watch the street. Without meaning at all.

XXIII

I've seen this man before, slumped against the same granite wall. The greasy jacket and trousers tied up with parcel string. He's unshaven, and what's left of his hair is an uncombed frizz. In front of him is the cap.

He puts the harmonica to his crusted lips, with fingers poking out of holes in a glove. He blows into the instrument, several discordant notes. Sucks the notes back. Blows.

At the same time he holds out his other hand, only it's a stump. Pink, tapering, rounded at the tip like a fleshy dibber. It slides smoothly from the sleeve.

He blows. Sucks. Not looking up. Holding the mouth organ between two forefingers and a thumb. Blows. Sucks.

Mostly he's passed by. Head bent at knee-level, he's unaware of the crowds.

Blows. Sucks. Urging out the pink dibber.

There's a few pennies scattered in the dirty hat.

He's saying you can choose. This may not be music. But this isn't a hand.

XXIV

The car park at the stadium where thousands of cars are arranged in lines. The stadium rises above it like a deep concrete dish for listening.

OOOOOOOOOOOOHHHHHHHHHHH

The cars are red, black, green, blue, yellow, red, black. Sunlight concentrates in flash-points on bonnets, roofs, chrome, mirrors.

There is the intense silence of a world of machines at rest.

AAAAAAAAAAAAAHHHHHHHHHHH

The shadow of the stadium works its way across one side of the car park, over the tarmac and the cars, soaking them in its coolth. They become dull and unnoticeable.

But most are beyond in the intense heat, shimmering like a mirage.

YYEEEEEEEEEEEEEEEEAAAAHHHHH

A man in shirt sleeves, hands in pockets, appears at the far end of the car park. He idles down one row, looking at the cars, bending to inspect a detail. The sun picks up the shine on the bald skin of his head.

He turns into the next row. Up. Next down.

No hurry.

He squeezes between two cars and leans awkwardly to one side to peer at a dashboard. He runs a finger up a slim, shining aerial.

Down one row. Up the next.

OOOOOOORRRGGGHHHHHHHHH

When he reaches the exit again the man turns, hands in pockets, surveying the glittering colour, breathing-in the engine smells in the heat.

Now he turns and walks off. His head bobs and shines past the bricked up shops with their faded names, Fruit & Veg, Ernies Caff, Second Hands, Iqbal Oriental.

OOOOOOOOOOOORRRRRGGGGGHHHHHHHHHHH

XXV

New names for the city. Not urbs or polis, or metro-polis. The ancient cities flourished as vividly as dreams cast against a glare. Stone lions and winged Victories and temple columns. To be trowelled out of the desert, brushed, picked clean, labelled, numbered, described, drawn. The ancient cities.

As for the city now, it has no adequate name. We can hardly start because we do not know where to begin. Many names. That which subsumes us. Within limits, no limits.

Up and down the streets the restless shoals of eyes, rushing to windows of shops, flick-glancing past eyes in advancing crowds, bobbing down dark entrances to stations, bars. Travelling. Moving. Forgetting.

Eyes that cannot stand the cold in other eyes.

That poor fellow with his legs splayed out staring up in a daze, past the surrounding crowd staring down, past the kneeling nun who keens over him like his own mother.

—Ah you poor fellow, poor man.

Pressing his hand.

Not looking past to the grey sky or the banks and the insurance buildings. Not thinking about the wine-flow of his blood as it stains into the paving.

—Ah you poor fellow, poor man.

Washed up, on the tides of the city.

The people are curious, watching the nun. Her robes are blue. Her headdress is crisp and white. Like peace. They have never seen such a thing before.

—Ah poor fellow. Poor man.

Pressing his hand.

This city cannot die while we live. Not like the others, the urbs or polis. It takes all our credos and that which we chose not to believe. It absorbs our blessings and builds on our cries. We are afraid of it. We have given it no name because we do not know what it is.

XXVI

It's time to be more emphatic. Assert himself.

— *You fucking bastards.*

The man sways, steadies himself against the concrete rim of the mall fountain.

That wasn't enough.

— *Fucking bastards.*

He swings the bottle. Upends it into his mouth. The grey stubble on his throat glitters silver as the muscles ripple and swallow.

He wipes his raw, red lips in a sleeve. Looks round as if he has a right to satisfaction

The shoppers swerve to give him a wide berth, like the invisible push between negative poles of magnets.

He's not satisfied. Not had enough.

— *You know what you are. Nothing but shit.*

He pushes himself away from the fountain, lurches on the paving stones of the mall.

— *What you looking at, you old bag.*

The woman shakes her head quickly from side to side in a tight-lipped tut-tut, refuses to acknowledge him except for the quicker pace of her steps and the way she clutches herself-to-herself to get away faster.

— Did you hear what he called her.

— Drunken sot.

The man walks stiffly back to the fountain, not bending at the knees. He upends the bottle briefly and tosses it in the basin. It floats for a while, bobbing on the surface, sucking in water through the neck until it's almost full, then slides gently to the bottom.

The man leans on the concrete rim, arms still, head hunched between his shoulders. He stares into the basin at the rippling bottle.

He swings round.

— *A man's a fool. A man's a fool to believe any of this.*

XXVII

—Did I kill her? Is she under the concrete of the patio? Am I walking across the remains of her face right now? Is she huddled there like archaeopteryx with a bony grasp on a grin? I remember nothing, so confess nothing, deny nothing. Are the police on my trail? Are they watching my door? If I phone out will they listen in? Is that rooftop flash from the glass of binoculars? "Yes, there he is." "Got him sir?" "Yes come and have a look." "Funny bastard." "A bad case of the jitters, of the nerves. A bad case of funk." "Shall we pick him up?" "Not yet. Let him stew. Hullo." "What is it?" "He's grasping himself with his hands. He's tearing himself apart." I can hear them. If I can't remember, how can I be guilty, but how can I be innocent. Release me from the city where every stone I tread covers a face.

XXVIII

The city is the reign of blueprints, master designs, potchings, substandard material, backhanders, never-mind-the-bloody-poor, sharp eyes in corridors, fast cars, technique, short-on-facts, good friends, firm handshakes, definite agreements, something on account, stick with us, good sort, trust me, this city's built on trust, graft, official announcements, Mr-Weber-can't-see-you-now, smiles, come ons, oh really, surveyors at dawn, hard hats and suits, it's a deal, jobs, the people need jobs, cut corners, fuck off sonny, barbed wire, sewage pipes, craters, concrete, steel mesh, don't-come-that-with-me, move-on-or-I'll-crush-your-balls, I'll-ave-you, essential flyovers, terraces erased, my-place-at-six-then, byee, marble façade, abandoned shuttering, puddles among rubble, didn't you know, for-fuck's-sake-shut-up, we're-doing-this-my-way, what's-in-it-for-me, I'll-see-you-alright, the-planning's-a-dawdle, in the pocket, in the bag, she's-alright-I-tell-you-she's-clean, fix-you-up-no-problem, anytime, pleasure-to-do-business, yes drinks-by-the-pool, shut up shut up for Chrissakes, shut up shut up shut up shut up.

XXIX

BURDENED MM WELL A, BURDENED OH YES A, BURDENED MY LORD A, BURDENED DONT YOU KNOW A, BURDENED OH GOD A, BURDENED YES I AM A, BURDENED HAVE MERCY A, BURDENED MM GOD A, BURDENED ALL MY LIFE A, BURDENED EVERY DAY A, BURDENED ALL THE TIME A, YES I AM A, OH YES A, MY LORD A, MM WELL A, HAVE MERCY A, HAVE MERCY LORD A, ON MY KNEES A, TRYING TO GET THROUGH A, IF YOU PLEASE A, THROUGH THIS STORM A, PERILOUS WATERS A, FAR FROM HOME A, CANT YOU SEE A, TIME AINT LONG A, OH MY LORD A, BURDENED YES A, CANT GO ON A, SINKING DOWN A, ON MY KNEES A, OH-LORD-OH-LORD A, OH-LORD-OH-LORD A, PRAYIN OUT, ON MY KNEES, OH HAVE MERCY, PRAY FOR ME, ON MY KNEES, MMMM, MMMM, MMMM, MMMM, MMMMMM

XXX

The churches have wire mesh over the windows and doors are locked. Someone's pissed against the wall. That's how it is. No use being a dreamer. The city rushes on, obsessed with its motion. If it stops it won't exist. It's not haste, super efficiency or speed, it's the embrace of dynamics. Jumping from the high board, doing the swallow. *Splash.* Feet disappear into water. Let's have it again. Replay. The screen goes fuzzy and the winding gear hums. *Click.* Arms raised. The spring. Swoop. *Splash.* Again. Nothing selfish at all in this, in the city. Not a race against time. Not out to make the rich or down the poor. *Haven't you learnt that mate. What it's all about. The free expression of form through space and time. The city as enlightenment of matter, settling for what is. That too much for you mate. "What about ME." Cut the CAPS mate. Don't mean a thing. Seen through personality. Don't hold with identity. Grow up. Get out of nappies. Cor strewth. "Mystics use the Side Entrance." Didn't you read the sign. It's a springboard, a release. Free fall. Let yourself go.*

XXXI

—Did you get that? Did you understand what he was saying? I don't think it's daft to ask "What about me?" He's saying we've abandoned identity in the city. That it all doesn't count. And I didn't like the implication about churches: if they're empty or abandoned it's because in some sense we're free. Do you agree with that? I don't. And all that stuff about dynamics and form. Even in crowds I still feel I know who I am. And who says the churches are empty? I read that religion's coming back. Not necessarily just Christianity. There's all kinds of means of approach to God. I think what he says denies a sense of mystery. Don't you? How does he know it's all energy and matter? Isn't it a bit arrogant? I still think there's room for the soul in the nature of things, and it's not disproved because I couldn't say what it is. I've always believed, if you know what I mean, after certain experiences which I'm inclined to call mystical. After all, you can't deny *self*, that you know you exist. And you can't help feeling afraid at the thought of your death. I see self as a plant with deep roots. The tap root is long and goes down into earliest memories. When I see photos of myself as a child, I think "Can that have been me?" But when I think back along the roots inside me, there're connections, part shadowy consciousness, part timid interplay of eagerness and fear. And what happens to self as you grow? It flowers, I feel, then seeds. And dies. And there's where I was about to say you have mystery. The seeds of the flowered, dying plant. To my mind, dry and almost weightless in the hand. But so much potential. I can't believe that all I've ever been can be utterly dead. The seed-pod rattles in the wind and shakes out the seeds. It can't all be on stony ground? No. Surely, though this isn't a vision, it's an intimation. It *has* to be true.

XXXII

—Harr. Humph. Blarr. A fair seedtime had my soul etcetera. Look yourself in the eye some morning when you're shaving. It'll tell you you're for it. Keep running by day and drink by night. The man with hollow legs. Remember old Comrade? He was a character. A real country boy. Never saw him drunk. Always seemed to sip from the rim of a pint while he looked across from an amused, quizzical face. Natty dresser too. You must remember him. Jacket and waistcoat, neat tie. And a buttonhole—marigold or carnation—filched from a garden. ''Well, better be off.'' ''Cheerio, Comrade.'' And he'd get on his big old black bike that he'd bought before the War and wobble out of town, shoulders stooping to the rhythm of the pedals. Like his drinking, he'd always seem to be slow but get there in the end. They say he beat his wife black-and-blue but we never saw that side of him. In the pub he was a quiet man, sipping at the rim of a glass, summing you up. Always a pint. Supping. Keeled over on a hill one day and found him dead in a hedge-bank, feet on the pedals.

—I remember him.

—Then I ask you, in all seriousness, where do you think he is now.

XXXIII

—I don't see any meaning among the quarks and hadrons. Some God-freak on his knees picks truth up by the tail: "I've got it! It's itty-bitty. The soul!" Make a Pascal Wager in reverse. Why not. Truth is that there's no meaning. So put on some threads. Adjust the shoulder pads. Brush the hair and pat the cheeks with a dab of Old Spice. Look cocky. Wotcha mate. Step into the bar. It's a lovely Sunday morning. "Here he comes! The Original Sunshine Man!" Wotcha Jimmy. A pint of your best, landlord, if you please. And slap the hands down sharp on the bar. Take out a packet of Navy Cut. Do a little tap-dance over to a table. Ave a coffin nail mate. "Ta, don't mind if I do." Be admired. Rake the tidfer at an angle and cakewalk down to your reflection in the full-length mirror. Johnny-by-Christ, you're a handsome devil! Come on everybody! Drink up! *Let's have fun!*

XXXIV

So good so far. I don't think life will let him get away with this, though. There's plenty of time for twists in the plot. He's done the best he can with that kind of ploy, stoical primitivism. I've nothing against it. But he thinks it's a hard act to follow or there's no act to follow. To an extent he's right, of course. The churches are sailing up mud creeks. Listen to their alarums. Exeunt. Alright for bishops abasing themselves at altars in stiff gold embroidery. And if you're a charismatic, charisma's the thing. Okey, too, for the tin-shed missionary shouting "Jesus! Yes, Lord Jesus!" All half-asleep and half-drugged with their dreams. I wouldn't walk down the street to rattle a stick against their railings. But the man with the cocky tidfer; I'm not sure about him. I don't know how long he can keep it up. He's not dancing with the Devil, as the mission-man might say. But by himself. He's alone, and that's where the trouble is. Look how it's boring through his eyes like the glow of charcoal. Behind the twinkle. He's making a game of it, I'll give him that. But he's running out of time. Could be like the Sailor in the last days of his cancer. *Get me out of here. Out of this body which no longer is mine. Can't you see it's me. It's Sailor. I'm here inside.* They had to put the safety rails up so his bed looked like a cage. Only hours to live. But the Sailor wouldn't go. He knew that after death he'd just be nothing. And he couldn't stand that. So he urged his body up out of the bed while nurses stood on tiptoe over him, leaning into the cage, trying to calm him down. "*Please,* Mr Evans," *Get me out of this. It's Sailor. I don't want to go.* As if, if only he could escape from this room, from these strangers, and run down the corridors into the street and run, run, he could be a little ahead of his body, as it were, when the terrible moment came. Then he would turn round, *Me, the Sailor,* head down, hands on knees, gasping and hawking, to look at his own dead flesh on the ground. *By Christ, that was a close one. That was a close-run thing.* Panting and sweating.

Look at this man, now, checking his reflection at the bar. He could be another Sailor, don't you suppose.

XXXV

—You're a canny beggar, aren't you. Trying to confuse people over their faith, undermine their identity. And blame it all on the city. Well I've news for you. There's millions of us, and we may have different beliefs—and I'm not saying there aren't bad apples—but basically we're one. All human. Now I don't suppose you know what that means. Each of us perishable, but in each something of worth, what's human. Yes, you're trying to wriggle out of it now. Won't look me in the eyes. At least you've got some sense of shame. What types like you don't realise is that you've *got* to believe. In something. I don't care what it is. Because without faith, you're not human, not one of us. That's how it is and how it's always been. And you're asking us not to be human. To put off humanity with knowledge. We've got to do something with our lives, not just torment ourselves. I'm not a Christian but I genuinely admire those who are. I wish I could go on my knees and pray like some of them. Sincere people who do a lot of good. What does it matter if what they believe may not be true. It's out there amongst life's poor and wounded that counts. So why don't you let them alone. The city's not half as bad as you say it is. I've lived here all my life and I don't feel a nonentity. I've never had difficulty believing in me. I think it's a shame that someone with education can't set an example. Your trouble is that you think too much. It'd be far better for you if you got out there and did some good.

XXXVI

In the Italia, the waiters are gearing themselves for a long evening. The pizza cook, who stands behind a glass counter, has prepared bowls of chopped tomato, peppers, mushrooms, olives, salami, parmesan and herbs.

His hands are floured up to the wrists, his fingers work briskly in the mound of malleable dough.

He bangs it on the marble work slab, pushes it left and right, lofts it and slaps it down. He scoops out a piece of the dough, moulds it with a few taps of the fingers, lifts it and pats it, circling it quickly between his palms. He throws the dough above his head with a spin to get the critical rotation. It descends on his forefinger, which he sends speeding out to the rim, twirling it, lowering and lofting it. *Angelo!* The waiter half way across the room, turns. The disc of dough is already flying towards him, rotating, wobbling. In his left hand the waiter carries a dish of pasta, another crooked on his forearm. He snaps up his right, spins his forefinger into the violently wobbling disc. He steadies it, brings up its speed, lofts it once, twice, to the ceiling, head moving beneath it like a snake in time to each motion. *Hey!* He spins it down to the floor, squatting on his knees, two dishes of pasta leaning on his forearm. Then lofts it. *Hey! Giovanni!*

The cook looks up. The disc of dough, bigger and thinner now, wobbles back quickly across the room.

At a glance the cook's got it, brought it down to the marble.

His fingers move like nimble sticks in and out of the bowls, shoulders working to the rhythm, head bent, not looking up. Dotting, sprinkling, dabbing, splashing.

Hey!

He slides a long-handled bread-spade under the pizza, snaps open the oven door, sweeps in the loaded spade and with a flourish sweeps it out.

Now he's back at the counter waiting for the next order. A glance at the bowls, at the dough. *Okey!* Under control.

Time to rest, his left hand on the marble slab, his right crooked at the waist, clutching a tea towel, looking across the tables, searching among diners for the pretty girls. *Oy-yoy-oy!* Eyes quizzical and mischievous. Ready to flirt. For a laugh. Ready to go.

XXXVII

The city has a lien on silence
    EAANNNWWNNGG
    The stunt plane dives vertically, pulls out into the base of the U
    EEEEEANNNNNN
    Pulls up vertically, taking the strain like a bird's heart
    Veins stand out at the temples with a message to the brain
    NNNNGGGGGGG
    Pull out
    The plane stands still on its tail
    Silence
    Flicks on its back
    The city is the dirty crowded sky
    Switch off
    PHHHHHHHHHHHHHHHHHHHHHHHHHHHHHHHHHHH
    The plane flips nose down
    Left wing up   left wing down   right wing up   right
wing down
    The pilot asks, Is this an act of the will
    The engine splutters and he pulls the plane out
    EEEAANNNNNGGGGHHH
    Going for height
    Flips back
    Enters the corkscrew
    Flick flick flick flick flick flick flick flick flick
    Look at the instruments   Look at the ground
    EEEAANNNNGGGGHH
    PHHHHHHHHHHHHHHHHHHHHHHHHHHHHHHHHHH

XXXVIII

```
Hullo          Yes        Yess          Speaking        Oh hello
Uh-hunh        Yes     Mmm       Yes        What did     Yes
Mm             I see       Mm          Mm-hmm             To
So you don't think       No      Well if       Yes        Mmm
Uh I           Have you    Ah-hunh        Oh by the        Mmm
Mm             MmmmYe         All           Alright          Ye
That's a       Mm       That's a date then        Ya       Mm
Well if        Ah-hunh        F           Fine             Fine
Yes sure       Ye      Ah-huh       After six        Ya    Mm-hm
Mm             Nice to      Yes        You too          Uh-hunnh
Okey           Ya       After          After six then          R
Yes            Yes uh-hunnh        Okey        Ya       After-uh six
Th             Yes            Th              Thanks for ringing
Ha-ha          Yes      Th      Thanks       Ha-ha       Yes      Bye
```

XXXIX

On top of the skyscraper two people play tennis in whites, behind green plastic-coated netting. One door, through which the players came, leads down into the building with its electric thrum.

—Come on darling, for God's sake, if we're playing.

The woman stands at the netting, clutching it with her right hand as she looks out over the city. Buildings are dissolved in a grey haze that swallows the trees except for the highest canopies. Up here, traffic is reduced to a hum.

—Are we playing or not.

—Yes. It's beautiful.

Not turning.

—Of course it's bloody beautiful. Now can we get on.

—You can see the river far out. It must be near the estuary. Almost where the city comes to an end.

—Oh for God's sake.

She turns.

He goes to the base line and crouches, cradling the neck of his racquet in his left hand, swaying slightly as he shifts the balance of his weight from side to side.

She bounces the ball, leaning forward, racquet held back, right arm slightly crooked.

Bounces the ball. Looks up. Makes as if to heave her body into the serve.

The man rises slightly, sways like a spider.

She catches the ball. Bounces it.

Once. Twice.

He rocks from left foot to right. Left to right.

She rises into the serve but hits too high and wide.

Second serve.

Bounce once. Twice. Three. Four.

He moves closer to the net.

Up into the serve. Pats the ball into the net.

—Oh come on. What the hell's the matter with you. Are we playing or not.

She walks away from him back to the netting; stands there absorbed by the hum and the misty fumes, softened geometric forms of buildings, where the river runs, something ancient and dull, until it emerges glittering on the horizon and enters the sea.

47

XL

TO THOSE WHO LEFT THE CITY AND NEVER RETURNED

A mother figure in granite bends over a child who gazes up with granite eyes.

It's in a grave-mound lined with granite blocks where a frieze in relief tells of the journey from the city.

A shaft in the roof lets daylight fall on the mother, enfolding her in a changing embrace of granite-pink shadows.

There's a dark hollow smell as if earth is seeping through the walls.

At the entrance an iron gate keeps people out, except once a year.

Then it is opened and those who come can wander round the mother in silence, or whisper explanations to a child.

But this isn't a holy place. It was built after the death of the spirit for those who left the city, who never returned.

XLI

Almost the loveliest thing in the city is the great building of pale smoky glass which stands like an impassive memorial to all hopes, where clouds float like grey angels, shadowed by the blinding force of the sun.

Almost the loveliest thing.

XLII

As I walk down a shady avenue on a summer day, I come across something strange. A car covered in artificial turf. The owner is making a point. He's saying we've finally severed our roots in nature. Cut right through. Feel it. The crinkly texture of plastic grass. You'll never get a lawn as close cropped as that, that looks so fresh and living and green. The owner is a celebrant of the city. It's up to us. We're travelling now. Some don't like it. But there's no avoiding the journey. And we didn't bring life rafts because we don't expect survivors. No point in half measures. Clean breaks are always the best.

XLIII

Who knows how the city works. No one knows. Not in the churches and the hills. The city is where the mystics have to be.

XLIV

Something like a ship. From the Rotunda on a clear day, when I think
I can see to the limits but cannot be sure, I imagine a creamy wake
flowing from the city in all directions, three hundred and sixty
degrees. But at the same time there's a bow slicing the hissing waters
of space and time in all directions. Movement outwards and inwards.
It's the journey. No way to change its direction, because it has none.
We sail with it. We must bear it. Hold on.

XLV

—I have to come back to this point. I just don't like your attitudes. You talk down to people who try to do their bit. That's not good enough. I know that the problems are huge but they're not insuperable if we all pull together. Every bit *does* count. You can't change people overnight. It takes time. But with perseverance and above all faith we can do it. But you haven't got much of that. You'd rather stand on the sidelines and sneer. We'd never get anywhere if people listened to you. I know things are bad but they're not hopeless. We use Ecover and bottle banks *and* paper banks. And both the wife and myself think twice now before using the car. We've got insulation and double glazing. I don't think you can get much more energy conscious than that. Alright. I'm not saying it's enough but it's a start. And I think we give an example. Only the other day our neighbour said "I see you use the bottle bank." I said yes. And he said, "You know, I think you're right, I was only saying to the wife last night, don't throw that wine bottle out, save it and put it in the garage, and when we've got a pile, I'll take them down the bank. I've noticed how they get filled up very quickly now. There's obviously something in it." Everybody's got to do their bit for the environment. It may not be much but it's a beginning. And people are like that. These things take time. And what you said about severing our ties with nature. That's a complete load of rubbish. Our boy's in the World Wildlife Fund and he loves tigers and pandas. And if we've severed our ties with nature, why are there so many nature programmes on TV, and why are they so popular? Besides, nature's coming back in the city. Only the other day I read how there are foxes everywhere and kestrels nesting in city churches. And somebody said there were rare birds becoming quite common in gardens. It's not all doom and gloom. All you do is depress people. But you've got to think positive and make people *believe* that things can be changed. And this thing about a journey. There's a lot of people have said that. You aren't the first. It's a very religious idea as a matter of fact. But you say it's a journey without an end (have I got that right?) and that there won't be any survivors. What kind of talk is that? Yes, life is a journey. But a journey of hope. And what did you mean by "after the death of the spirit"? There you go again. You've said that before and I think it's a very negative way of looking at things. Like I said, how can you prove it. You can't. And this journey that the city's supposed to be on. How can it be like a ship sailing in two directions at once. That's clever talk to me. It sounds good but what does it mean. I believe things *will* change. It'll take time, of course. But we mustn't give up. If you've got children, you have to have hope. You have to think of their future. I don't believe personally that the human race can ever die out. What you are is a terrorist. Yes, that's it. A terrorist of the mind. Undermining life. Well it won't work. I can tell you that. And I'll tell you something else for free. You're on your own.

XLVI

The rubbish tips. Dumper trucks and garbage collection wagons bump over the makeshift approach road of cinders, dipping and splashing in the rain-filled ruts and potholes. Piles of waste spill out like viscera. Black bags mauled open. That which cannot be used. Sliced out of the carcass. Then the yellow JCBs move in, pushing the rubbish, the tumbling piles, until it is flat. The dump builds up. Pushed flat by the JCBs. Black-headed gulls alight and snatch and just flick off out of the paths of the purposeful blades. And the dump rises on three sides, a perfect scarp, pushed deeper and deeper into what's left of the marsh, black bags toppling into the reeds. Fires start here and there. Long smouldering trails of smoke. And here come more dumper trucks, more lorries, more JCBs. There's a sense of toil, of getting things done. Beyond, blurred by the smoke, the tenements. The gulls swoop, wheel, tear, tug, stab, scold for the scraps. The sky is whirled by the white of their wings. The unstoppable anger of their cries. The men in the JCBs in blue donkey jackets are silent inside the sealed room of the engine's roar. At night when the machines are parked on the skyline, there's a truce, a kind of peace. Smoke drifts down the wind. There are the lights of tenements and the dotted lights of streets that run out and trail nowhere. Fences topped by barbed wire. The red flicker of a glow from spontaneous combustion deep in the tip. And nosing in plastic yoghourt cups, bean tins, frozen dinner trays, the nimble, furred faces of the rats, with sensitive nostrils, insatiable eyes.

XLVII

The night security guard sits with his feet up in his office. It's two in the morning and time for a break. A white mug of tea steams on the table at his elbow. He enjoys the night shift. He likes being alone. As he waits for the tea to cool, he leafs through yesterday's paper. In the window to his left are strings of lights that glare fuzzy yellow along the motorway flyover that passes the factory, where the oblong box-shapes of all-night lorries moan past to the city. A fitter walks by in a boiler suit, carrying a tool bag. He stops in mid-stride and looks in through the open door.

—Hey Charlie, why don't you get a job like the rest of humanity!

The security guard makes as if to lift his legs off the table. Looks mock-offended. Then lowers them again.

—What would you know about work, Bri. You've never tried it.

The fitter laughs.

—See you.

—Hey, Bri.

As the fitter moves out of the brittle frame of neon light in the office doorway.

The guard holds his paper inside pages facing out for the fitter to see.

—How'd you like to get up that.

56

XLVIII

The cathedral squats among tower blocks. It was on a journey once but the charts were wrong. Confident they could draw a line through time and space. Terror and pain on the way but ending in the approach roads to the harbour. That beacon on the headland, I'm sure I recognise it, and rounding the point with the land's shining fields and farms, there it is. Two semi-circular walls project like an embrace. The entrance is narrow but to be safely negotiated this day.

Now they sell postcards and pamphlets explaining its jumbled history. If that bit's thirteenth century then that bit must be fourteenth. And what's a clerestory?

There remains a sense of musty awe, the keep-your-hands-out-of-your-pockets kind, or a verger might come and tick you off. "This *is* God's house. Show a little respect, please, even if you don't believe."

A place to be bored in. Where millions who never asked to be born into space-time hoped Christ on the Cross had cut a line through like oxy-acetylene, creating a door out of this horror and mess.

But all the icons I've ever seen are of man.

XLIX

Why she killed herself isn't really a mystery, though I'm surprised personally that she had the courage. Because it does take courage, no matter what people say about cowardice, not facing up to things, and what about those who are left behind who have to pick up the pieces and carry on. I don't hold with that view. They're the selfish ones, thinking if someone close to me did it how would *I* feel. Anyway, she didn't have anyone very close that I know of. But still I'm surprised that she did it. Her head in the gas oven. Lay in the oven entrance after taking out all the racks. Like lying in the black doorway to everlasting hell. Only to her it wasn't. Hell was where she was and the door was her exit.

She had a very pleasant flat, old and roomy, with high moulded ceilings. That nineteenth-century sense of spaciousness. It was in a good quarter near the city centre.

Outside, there was an avenue of very old lime trees. Their canopies reached well up to her second floor windows and were a beautiful rich rustling green in summer, though I always felt they had a stark, pitiless air about them when the leaves had fallen.

There's no doubt about it, it was a nice place to live. Even if you were unhappy, you'd think, drawing the curtains in the evening, and maybe settling down in an easy chair to read a book, or thinking, no, there's no point, I can't concentrate, and put on some Brahms instead. Even if you were unhappy, curled up in the easy chair, with soft light from the standard lamps and soft shadows on the ceiling, the fitted white bookcase with all the books she liked, you'd think she'd think, I may be unhappy now, but nothing lasts, and this isn't a sad but a good place to live. And then she'd reach out for the handle of the small cup of black Java coffee that she always drank, its surface shining like a black, polished stone.

That's what most of us would do. As we say, we all live in hope. Life may not be much at the moment but there's bound to be an upswing. And things do look better in the morning. After breakfast, down to the shops for bagsful of onions, tomatoes, aubergines, courgettes; then to the butcher's where he'll be sharpening his knives on a steel. "Now then, madam, what can I do you for on this beautiful sunny morning." Have you noticed how butchers are always cheerful, surrounded by death.

Saturday mornings can seem quite pleasant. That casual contact. "Hullo. How are you. I haven't seen you lately. Not ill I hope. No.

Good. Me? No, I'm fine. Well nice seeing you. Must dash.'' That sort of thing. And the cars. The build-up of traffic after about ten. It gives a sense of purpose, of things going on. Colour and noise, a sense of being alive. Almost a thrill.

Not complicated thought. Not the mind undermining itself, or running down.

Some days I've felt like staying indoors the whole weekend. Lock myself away. But a trip to the shops and I always feel better. And after lunch maybe a walk in the park. Or just feet up on the balcony, reading a novel. It can't be bad, that sort of existence. Reaching out for a coffee cup it's hard not to think, this is the life.

But then comes evening. The thickening of the light, the twilight despair. Did you know that at dusk baboons climb up among the rocks by themselves and howl. They howl till the sun's gone down. I read that in a book by a man who studied them for years. And in the end he shot himself. The twilight despair.

I used to feel it a lot when I was younger. Though not so much now. An intensity, a panic. I had to get moving, get out, do anything to escape this light thickening into gloom.

I'm not saying she felt that. I don't know. But think of her sitting there, looking out over the tops of the canopies to the lights coming on in the flats opposite. Everyone else's lights seem more attractive, warm, relaxed than your own; people at peace with themselves and each other. It's not true of course, but that's how it seems.

And you're alone, locked into the self, no matter how tasteful the surroundings. No, I'm not saying it was what makes the baboons howl from the rocks, but she put the book face-down on the table, left the unsipped cup of black coffee, took the pick-up off the Brahms and switched off the lights.

Then she went into every room where there was a mirror and covered it with a sheet or a towel.

As I say, after that she went into the kitchen, opened the oven door, took out the racks and turned on the gas. She lay there curled up on her right side, facing the tall kitchen window which from that angle, and at that time in the evening, would have seemed gaunt, and through it she would have seen the occasional light in a kitchen among the top floor flats that backed onto hers.

So I'd been wrong. She'd had the courage after all.

L

Five to ten million years is quite good for a species. But in the city we don't think like that. Species, what species. We're something else. With the steel and the glass. The lights, power-lines, circuits, motorways, cars. Come on don't give me that stuff about *species*. City-us. You may say the city is nothing by itself. Nor are we. City-us. No blueprint. None of it planned. But it happened and there's no turning back. So no regrets. We are here. City-us. Leave it and you're dead. Oppose and we'll kill you. Yes we're here. No blueprints. No plans. Symbiosis. City-us.

LI

—Have you thought of the tons of human meat that's needed to make this place go. In all these rooms, under all these lights, in all these streets. Has anyone ever weighed it? The immense quantities of human meat that are needed to keep the city alive. It must be hundreds of thousands, even millions of tons. That's a thought. To keep things going. Each of us thinking, when we think of it at all, "Well, at least it's *me*." You can if you like say "Well, I don't experience the city like that at all. There's the neighbourhood, for a start. All the neighbours and friends. And there's always some relation living within reach." But really we swim in an Arctic sea where faces are krill. Stop in the street when you see someone you recognise. Go home and think, "Well, yes, I can carry on." But it's meat all the same in offices and shops, in factories, when all's said and done. And in bars. I'll be alright. Just another pint. It's nothing. Do you think I can't hold another fucking pint. It's nothing, I tell you. I'm a man who likes his drink, that's all. It's nothing. Can't a man have another pint. Go to fucking hell.

IT'S THE ROBINSON JEFFERS SHOW!

Hello. It's Robinson Jeffers here. Speaking. (Is this thing working?) I told you in my works what you needed to know. I foretold what should already have been plain. (Are you sure it's on?) I knew you wouldn't heed me. I knew you would do nothing. Hello. Hello. It's Ro- (Are we on the air?) I knew because I know the nature of the species. How we have to act out our murderous lives to the end. Not tragic. Desperate. I saw it from the tower on the cliffs. Went there to escape you. Grandeur of ocean, of clouds. The brown mountains in pleats and folds. Couldn't escape you. Always in my thoughts. Tearing each other up in my mind. Foresaw the real estate. Thought I was a god, or close to a god, before my wife died. Brought me down. The steps of the tower. You all know a little about sorrow. Grief will kill you, get you down to skin and bones, like Buddy Doyle said. I foresaw the freeways and the highways. Knew you'd outpace yourselves. Had *already* outpaced yourselves. Taken yourselves for a ride. Not tragedy. Wouldn't feed you winter grain to keep you alive for that. Read the poems. Saw it all from the tower. There like a God. Until she died. Saw it all, and let it happen. Turned away to the west, to the red shattering sunset across the sea. I was a god. And then she died. Down those steps. One by one. I built them all. But didn't give up. Despised myself as much as I despise you. *Turn away.* Nothing can be done to stop what's happening. *Turn away.* Don't listen to the men in suits with microphones. Not the mouth-wash talk. And not the green pull-together talk. If it's got to be green, then deep deep green. Then dark green where nothing else grows. Not Gaia talk. *Do you hear me.* But dark talk. *Turn away.* It you want to live with whatever of dignity's left. Let the human species be devoured. Self-damned and devoured.

This is Robinson Jeffers. I hope you liked the show. Anyone out there capable of listening. Anybody out there. The Robinson Jeffers show.

Sation WXK—101, the station that brings you green news before it happens.
Stay tuned folks. Don't go away. Coming up next—South of the Border. Yes,
the best in Tex-Mex with Los Hermanos Chavarria and their latest hit "Quiero
Que Sepas"; your favourite and mine El Ciego Melquiades (have you heard his
"Quisiera Llorar"); and yes, you've guessed it, Lydia Mendoza, La Goria de
Texas, singing and playing all your favourites, "Noche Tenebrosu y Fría",
"Mundo Engañoso", "Sigue Adelante", "La Boda Negra", "Tu Ya No
Soplas". Stay tuned. For the best in Tex-Mex, after this short annoucement from
our sponsors, California International Oil. Stay tuned. After the break.

—Was that okey?

—That was great, Robinson.

—(Jeez where did you get this guy?)

—(I thought he'd be okey. For Chrissakes, the guy's being hailed as a Green before his time. He's the godfather of the Dark Greens, for Chrissakes.)

—(*Dark* Greens. What is this. The first April? You tryin to put me on or something? What's with this Dark fuckin Greens? I wanted some shit about don't throw away your Coke cans.)

—(Don't blame me. The guy was supposed to have been a Green before his fuckin time. He was supposed to have been cool. How'd I know he'd come over heavy.)

—(*Green.* SHIT.)

—Was that okey?

—Yeah Robinson. It was just great.

63

LIII

The man in flames. Can't believe this. Runs towards people in the streets, arms open, appealing. They step back. Aghast. Shirt streams flames as he runs. Burning. Hair. Skin. Can't believe. Still see with eyes the look in eyes of others. As if mirrors for his own.

Knew things could happen. But never to him.

Stumbles. Down heavily on both palms. Flat on pavement. A spring with toes, calf muscles. Amazing what can do.

Up. Still working. Running. Can't believe this.

Look. Mirrors in eyes. Not too much. Don't want to see this.

Down. Nessus. Back of the mind. Outstretched. Shirt in shreds.

Nessus. Down. Don't want to see this.

Down.

Ma.

Burned out.

Crowds.

Palm after palm. Knees.

Ma. Reduced.

Never expected.

This.

As he crawls. Burnt out man.

Scorched arm raised. Hand follows. Salute. This. Heu!

Whites of the eyes like blood-red-veined marble.

This.

Remember.

Never forget.

Burnt out man.

LIV

Powerlines looped across country between pylons like grand old ladies in whalebone-hooped frames of skirts. As if at a dance where elegance had been replaced by gauntness. Once they would have turned back to each other with a smile. But now a grimace. Sometimes a bird perches on the lines as if to think, then flits away across the fields leaving the pylons to the dance. They can never be free to let go the cables clamped to their hands, linking each skeleton to each. Across the skyline, over the large empty fields. Look how they step delicately among houses that cluster and thicken at the city's edge. It's as near as we come to religious art, the gaunt old ladies linking hands with the powerlines in their dance.

LV

Harry Martinson looks out of the opened window. We're on a journey, he says. And we've come a long way. And this one's different, because there's no turning back, stepping off or aside, waving to others who have undertaken to travel on.

I used to believe in a different journey of the world nomad who would be at home anywhere. I felt like that when I was young. Worked on ships. believed, too, in vagabonds. (Have you read *Vägen till Klockrike? Resor utan mål?* No? Not in your language yet. But if you had, you'd know.)

I don't see that I was wrong, in a way. I didn't romanticise what I knew myself was hard. But it was an idea, the world nomad, at home any place, any time.

However, the idea was linked with nature, don't you see. And though I saw the rain forest and the pampas, nature was *natur*, was *Sverige*, Sweden. The whispering rustle of the great tracts of trees. And the purple hummocks of the heather on the heaths, mile after mile.

The nomads for me were the poor. Even those who stayed in one place. There's all kinds of travelling of the mind. Those people on the farms, working themselves and others to death.

No, I didn't romanticise them. I was brought up on such farms. Yet there was something there that was different from the regimen of the city that I met in the stokeholds. Something intact. I had to hold irreconcilable ideas in my mind. I hated those farms, yet I admired them.

Everyone's on the journey from life to death but not all are among the nomads, cutting off to journey on their own, taking the ostracism and the spite, the scorn. Meeting their kind now and again but parting at crossroads, or deciding to slip off across the ploughed fields to the woods.

The susurration of trees in a northern summer. And stars like ancient survivors, so many years ago, above my head.

Impossible now.

It nearly broke me when they planted the heaths.

You can't be a nomad on a four-lane highway, dignity subsumed in the *flash flash-flash* of vehicles, their occupants' eyes on the speedo, losing the solitary man as a dwindling speck in rear-view mirrors.

I knew the world of speed would overtake me, when I was a youth in the stokeholds.

66

Tillintetgjord.

I believe I was right, but a man's beliefs are a grief when the age is against him.

They say there are some who still read my books. I don't know. Lonely people, perhaps. But for the rest, the city's journey, blocked out with lights from the nation of stars.

He closes the window. It's still early spring and a little chilly. He walks across the oriental carpet and sits at his desk. Poses for the photographer, as asked.

Rests his cheek on his right palm.

So his face is inclined at an angle as he looks into the camera and smiles.

LVI

—Personally, I'd give up the car tomorrow, if I could. There's no pleasure in driving these days. But it's a Catch-22, isn't it. Public transport's so run down. We use unleaded petrol, of course, and I'm hoping these catalytic converters (*is* that right? *Is* it catalytic/cathalytic? I'm never quite sure), as I say, I'm hoping they'll come down in price. I'd have one fitted then, because they say it'd make a lot of difference. But at the moment I don't see how we can manage without two. It's terrible, isn't it. I need one to get to work and Jan has to get the kids to school and do the shopping. Then there's her mother who's nearly senile. She keeps going but Jan has to visit her every day. I'm afraid it would be a home for her if we couldn't do that. But we're sparing as much as possible. Apart from the pollution there's the expense. And have you tried parking in the centre lately? A nightmare I can assure you. No, there's no pleasure in motoring any more. We've only got them because they're a necessity. Part of the modern way of life, let's face it. A necessary evil, you might say. But yes, we are concerned, and we're trying to do more.

LVII

—I'm not finished yet. I'm not finished yet.

They found him after he'd been lying three days on the floor. So weak from whiskey and lack of food, he couldn't move. Weighed eight stone.

Got him in bed at the hospital and took off his clothes. Sooner them than me. Nobody knew when he'd changed them last.

—I'm not finished yet. Not finished yet.

Plenty of fight in him.

And his nails curled right under his toes with a thick rime of dirt.

—I'm not finished yet. I'm not finished yet.

Alright. You bastard.

Too weak even to sit up and sip the broth they tried to persuade him to eat.

—You fucking leave me alone. I'm not finished yet.

—Of course you're not finished yet. You don't think we're keeping you here, I hope.

—Who do you think you're fucking talking to. Don't you know. I've been round the world. Round the fucking world. Seen more things than you've dreamed of.

—Come on. Eat some of this.

—I'm strong. Do you think I could have seen the things I've seen and not be strong. Fuck off.

And it would go on like this, until in the end they'd leave him.

—Alright, have it your way. You're on your own.

—Of course I'm on my fucking own. Go to Hell.

He'd toss his head from side to side with its grey locks. This way and that on the pillow. Lift his right hand at the wrist, drop it on the sheet. Lift it, drop it. As if tapping out, I'm not finished yet. Then stop. Start again. Lift the hand at the wrist and drop it. I'm not finished yet. Do you fuckers hear. Not finished yet.

LVIII

EPIGRAPHS FOR AN END

Man on this earth is an unforseen accident which does not stand close investigation.

Heyst

Every age is fed on illusion, lest men should renounce life early and the human race come to an end.

Conrad

LIX

FROM GUSTAV'S DIARY

People crowded the beach. The ship, a barque, was close inshore and beat for a while to the south. But before long, it ran aground on a sandbank, after which it turned slowly till the bows faced north. Waves broke over it in endless lines.

On the beach, lifeboatmen set up a breeches buoy, because it was impossible to put out in the boat.

They fired a rocket which fell in the sea a good way short of the barque. A couple more. Same result.

By now the masts had gone and the ship was a wreck.

The crew kept to the afterdeck but were reduced to a very few men. Nearly every wave took someone with it.

Now the barque began to list shoreward till the starboard rail was underwater. The crew members disappeared one by one. Then, when there were only three or four left, a man detached himself from the others and made his way midships, stepping sideways, clutching the port rail that stood high out of the water.

As he struggled, several waves broke over him, but he clung on till he reached a position midships where he could lash himself securely. Soon he was the only man on the barque.

With each breaker he was struck to the deck. Yet he raised himself again, and again, clearly visible against the wave-struck boards.

But there came a time when he no longer struggled up, and as more waves broke over the barque, he went the same way as his companions.

The last man had gone overboard.

LX

Alright. If we're on a journey, let's get going. No use being blind. Up and go. Cut the weepy eyes and the wishing we'd never left the quay. The past is dead. Only us-now and the future. Do you want to live the rest of your life in regret. Think you can get off light with a life-jacket. Reverse the course. Bullshit. The compass needle's at a steady F for Future. Steady as I've seen. Forget uncertainties. Don't be deceived by doubt. Try to throw a rope to "maybe" or "perhaps". All once-upon-a-time. Harden yourself, or go below. What's needed is the mask. The heat shield. And a slot to see through to the glare. Finished as a species. So what. Alright. But look at the glare, or finished as you and me. Stay on the bridge. Crowd to the bows. Look ahead. Put on the mask. See through the slit. Dawn's rising. We'll meet it coming over the treadmill of the Earth.

II

AFTERWARDS

Most people arrive
to gather on the shore
with packages
and children. The fighter

that nosed in
like the air's curious
fish, bled itself thin
over the hills.

"Here we are."
The bald statement
like the man, who shoulders
a suitcase and takes

a son by the arm. They
disappear over Earth's
trails. Did you ever
see things so strange.

STONY

Don't be surprised
by the lapidary
style of their lives.
They weren't great readers.

It's a puzzle
what they believed, and whether
they felt a surge
transforming to fear.

Calm night after rain
the houses glistened
and dripped. They were safe.
I thought I heard

explosions, but it was
only the town's fireworks,
celebrating
the will to go on.

CATASTROPHE

The family in black
like an embroidery. I can see
the mother, the serious
father, and the child.

Nobody holds
its hand. The faces are white
and European.
I know where they

collected such angst.
Centuries grip
them at the collar.
Even if they've left

the land, and the man
manages a stern
degree of fortitude,
the backs of the eyes

flash fear. Elusive
as creatures startled at
night, I think
they're beautiful.

CLEARING FORESTS

from the coast
until the mountains
slow them down. My
friends! Bad habits
like a clap on the shoulder—
"He's a good un"—
Shaking trees from their sockets
like weeds
piled into flames.
Neighbourly, they move on.

AT A PARTY

"The man who broods is lost,"
he sipped his drink.
"I'd almost like to say it isn't true."
Nodding a deprecating smile,
he turned and steered through knots of guests
holding his glass by its stem
at shoulder height.
In the sombre barque of his expensive suit
he had the grace of a fat man
who dances well.

YES

Every day, now,
an experiment,
giving new meaning
to the world *culture.*
Wherever I look
bacilli
multiply in rods
no faith can explain.
It's a hard shining.

BIG STORM

Tell them about me
when the masks
are down. "Can I
get through." Yes.
Water seethes
over the breakwater.
"Shall I hold." Yes
hold. "Shall I
hold." Yes, hold.

SURVIVAL

I can't party any more—
that squaring of the shoulders.
What are the gaps between
physics and me? The soul's
melted away like Wordsworth's
cloud. On all the ridges of these hills
I've walked with the ants
on the blade of a bone.

ANGLE

Each room has a mirror,
for a small town likes to see
itself as art, Dutch interiors
the outposts of their spare
design. I've seen too many
betrayals from the walls
and had enough of eyes
reversed, demanding something
with a glancing blow,
that nothing ever said
made me prepared to give.

SMALL TOWN

The umbilical accord
is broken. "What have I done
to deserve you being here.
They're so good to me,
my boys." Better than daughters?
"Yes. Yes. Oh everybody knows me
in the streets. Reputation,
the chink of solid coin
thrown down." Wheel her out,
a queen among servants.

MOTHER

''Help!
Do you think I'm
a bucket or
a shelf? I'm
down with the stone
worms. In a few
years your memories
will coalesce.
The camera
lucida will
reconstruct me. I'll
be, ghostly as
a window for souls.''

REALITY

I wear my face now
like a shield though
I cannot prevent
the heat loss from my

eyes. "Where were you
when you needed
me most?" Mother sit
back and let us

admire the grace
you have acquired.
Twisted and old like
seawood in the sand.

END

She didn't want to die,
but a great force
pushed her out beyond the mask.
"Oh it's like breathing air
from a cold blue sky."
Her face was impassive
in the morgue.

FLOWERS

Keep on,
they say from their wounds,
how can you turn back,
we press you to the edge
with softness
that embodies no more than our lives
leaning into the future.